PAUL HINDEMITH

DER SCHWANENDREHER

Concerto after old Folksongs
for Viola and Small Orchestra
Konzert nach alten Volksliedern
für Viola und kleines Orchester

T0080492

Ernst Eulenburg Ltd

London · Mainz · Madrid · New York · Paris · Prague · Tokyo · Toronto · Zürich

CONTENTS / INHALT

PREFACE / VORWORT

Paul Hindemith wrote his third viola concerto – which he gave the strange and memorable title *Der Schwanendreher* after the tune he used in the last movement – during a period of political hostility and informing. It was a time also of aesthetic and stylistic reorientation, which led him too to work out a theory of music of his own and to plan and perform his compositions with an increased sense of responsibility. In December 1934 Goebbels attacked him publicly. Defenceless, Hindemith found himself unexpectedly dragged into the centre of a cultural-political debate and increasingly isolated. The leading viola player of his time, he was given virtually no more engagements in Germany, and at the few performances of his works in the Third Reich – all the more spectacular for their rarity – the momentum of public demonstration against the political powermongers was growing. Hindemith could not yet make the decision to leave Germany but he had to transfer almost all his musical activities to foreign countries. In April/May 1935 he travelled, primarily in Turkey, and wrote extensive 'Suggestions for constructing the musical life of Turkey'. On 27 July 1935 he finished the opera *Mathis der Maler*, without any indication that a performance would be possible. In June 1935 he had already started the Sonata in E for violin and piano which he then finished in August; with this, he embarked – unconsciously as yet – on the famous series of sonatas for virtually all the conventional instruments of the orchestra. Nevertheless, in August Hindemith wrote four piano songs to texts by Angelus Silesius, and a piece for trautonium.

Paul Hindemith schrieb sein drittes Bratschenkonzert, dem er nach dem im letzten Satz verwendeten Lied den seltsamen, einprägsamen Titel *Der Schwanendreher* gab, in einer Zeit der politischen Anfeindungen und Denunziationen und der ästhetisch-stilistischen Neuorientierung, die ihn nun auch zur Ausarbeitung einer eigenen Musiktheorie führte und ihn seine Kompositionen in größter Verantwortlichkeit planen und ausführen ließ. Im Dezember 1934 griff ihn Goebbels öffentlich an. Unvermittelt und wehrlos sah sich Hindemith in das Zentrum kulturpolitischer Auseinandersetzungen gezerrt und immer stärker isoliert. Als der führende Bratscher seiner Zeit überhaupt erhielt er in Deutschland kaum mehr Engagements, und den wenigen, dafür umso spektakuläreren Aufführungen seiner Werke im „Dritten Reich" wuchs das Moment der offenen Demonstration gegen die politischen Machthaber zu. Hindemith konnte sich zunächst noch nicht dazu entschließen, Deutschland zu verlassen, doch mußte er seine musikalischen Aktivitäten nahezu ausschließlich ins Ausland verlagern. Im April/Mai 1935 bereiste er erstmals die Türkei und verfaßte umfangreiche *Vorschläge zum Aufbau des türkischen Musiklebens*. Am 27. Juli 1935 schloß er die mühevolle Arbeit an der Oper *Mathis der Maler* ab, ohne daß sich Möglichkeiten einer Aufführung abzeichneten. Bereits im Juni 1935 hatte er die *Sonate in E* für Violine und Klavier begonnen, die er dann im August vollendete und mit der er – noch unbewußt – jene berühmte Serie von Sonaten für nahezu alle gebräuchlichen Orchesterinstrumente eröffnete. Ebenfalls noch im August komponierte Hindemith vier Klavierlieder nach Texten von Angelus Silesius sowie ein Stück für Trautonium.

In the following holiday month of September, which Hindemith and his wife spent in Brenden (Black Forest), Winterthur (where he met Paul Valéry), Beuron and Frankfurt, the viola concerto *Der Schwanendreher* appeared, apparently the result of a spontaneous idea. He finished the score in Berlin on 13 October 1935. According to the sequence of sketches, Hindemith composed the final movement first, then the middle movement, and lastly the opening movement. At the beginning of November he played the solo part of the concerto through for the first time: 'I am busily practising the concerto', he wrote on 6 November 1935 to the music publisher B. Schott's Söhne in Mainz. 'It seems to be pretty. But it is well known that it is always dangerous for composers to fall into the clutches of performers.'[1]

The first performance, also broadcast, was given in Amsterdam on 14 November 1935 by the Concertgebouw Orchestra conducted by Willem Mengelberg. Hindemith not only played the solo viola but also conducted the *Philharmonisches Konzert* (1932) beforehand. In fact, work on the viola concerto was not quite finished for, in July 1936, when Hindemith made the piano score of the work, he constructed a completely new ending to the third movement (bars 279ff). Hindemith first played the concerto in this new definitive form on 13 September 1936 in Venice (conducted by Fernando Previtali, whom Hindemith held in high esteem). It was overwhelmingly successful. Until 1939 he performed the concerto in Europe and in the USA, always with great success, with such renowned conductors as, for example, in 1936/7, Alfredo Casella, Ernest Ansermet, Othmar Schoeck, Oswald Kabasta, Arthur Fiedler, Artur Rodzinski, Erich Kleiber and George Szell; in 1939 he recorded the work on disc

Im folgenden Urlaubsmonat September, den Hindemith mit seiner Frau in Brenden (Schwarzwald), Winterthur – hier traf er sich mit Paul Valéry –, Beuron und Frankfurt verbrachte, entstand offenbar aus einem plötzlichem Einfall heraus das Bratschenkonzert *Der Schwanendreher*. Am 13. Oktober 1935 schloß er in Berlin die Partitur ab. Nach der Chronologie der Skizzen komponierte Hindemith zunächst den Schlußsatz, dann den Mittelsatz und zuletzt den Kopfsatz. Anfang November spielte er erstmals den Solopart des Konzertes durch: „Ich übe fleissig am Konzert", schreibt er am 6. November 1935 an den Musikverlag B. Schott's Söhne, Mainz, „es scheint hübsch zu sein. Bekanntlich ist's ja stets etwas gefährlich für Komponisten, den Spielern in die Fänge zu geraten."[1]

Die von Rundfunkstationen übertragene Uraufführung des Werkes fand am 14. November 1935 in Amsterdam mit dem Concertgebouw Orchester unter der Leitung von Willem Mengelberg statt. Hindemith spielte nicht nur die Solobratsche, sondern dirigierte zuvor auch noch sein *Philharmonisches Konzert* (1932). Freilich war damit die Arbeit am Bratschenkonzert noch nicht ganz abgeschlossen; denn als Hindemith im Juli 1936 den Klavierauszug des Werkes herstellte, gestaltete er den Schluß des III. Satzes (T. 279ff.) völlig neu. In dieser neuen, definitiven Fassung spielte Hindemith das Konzert erstmals am 13. September 1936 in Venedig (Dirigent: Fernando Previtali, den Hindemith sehr schätzte) mit überwältigendem Erfolg. Bis 1939 führte er das Konzert in Europa und den USA stets überaus erfolgreich mit namhaften Dirigenten auf – z.B. 1936/37 mit Alfredo Casella, Ernest Ansermet, Othmar Schoeck, Oswald Kabasta, Arthur Fiedler, Artur Rodzinski, Erich Kleiber

---

[1]Extracts from letters are taken from unpublished letters preserved in the Paul-Hindemith-Institut, Frankfurt/M.

[1]Die Briefzitate stammen aus unveröffentlichten Briefen, verwahrt im Paul-Hindemith-Institut, Frankfurt/M.

in the USA. Hindemith never played his concerto in Germany and even after the Second World War he conducted it only once in that country – in Berlin (1962).

In the first movement Hindemith uses the song 'Zwischen Berg und tiefem Tal', which, like all the other songs in this concerto, he took from Böhme's *Altdeutsches Liederbuch* (Böhme No. 163):

oder Georg Szell; 1939 spielte er in den USA das Werk auf Schallplatte ein. In Deutschland hat Hindemith sein Konzert freilich nie gespielt und es in diesem Land nach dem 2. Weltkrieg auch nur einmal in Berlin (1962) dirigiert.

Im ersten Satz verwendet Hindemith das Lied *Zwischen Berg und tiefem Tal*, das er, wie auch alle anderen Lieder dieses Konzertes, Böhmes *Altdeutschem Liederbuch* (Böhme Nr. 163) entnahm:

First Hindemith sketched the main sections of the movement – bars 34–214 (end of movement), which is a modified sonata form: main theme (bars 34–60) in C, subsidiary theme (bars 61–95) in G, closing theme (bars 96–123) with the folk melody in dorian mode on A, developmental reprise (bars 124–207) with an extended cadence (bars 184–192) which is thematically derived from the subsidiary theme, short coda (bars 208–14). As climax of the movement Hindemith originally planned, in bars 174ff, the following contrapuntal combination of the three themes contained within the movement (they are crossed out in the sketches):

Hindemith skizzierte zunächst den Hauptteil des Satzes mit den Takten 34–214 (Satzende), der eine modifizierte Sonatensatzform trägt: Hauptsatz (T. 34–60) in C, Seitensatz (T. 61–95) in G, Schlußgruppe (T. 96–123) mit der Liedweise in A-dorisch, durchführungsartige Reprise (T. 124–207) mit auskomponierter Kadenz (T. 184–192), die thematisch vom Seitensatz zehrt, knappe Coda (T. 208–214). Als Höhepunkt des Satzes sah Hindemith ursprünglich in den Takten 174ff. folgende, in den Skizzen durchgestrichene kontrapunktische Vereinigung der drei den Satz tragenden Themen vor:

Only then did Hindemith add the slow introduction with the viola solo (bars 1–10)

Er fügte dann erst die langsame Einleitung mit dem aus der Kadenz abgeleiteten Brat-

VI

derived from the cadence and the folk melody, dorian on C, (bars 11–33) in the character of a funeral march, which establishes the style of the whole work.

In the quiet outer sections of the second movement (bars 1–72 and 219–61, in A in each case) Hindemith introduces the mixolydian song 'Nun laube, Lindlein, laube' (Böhme No. 175):

schensolo (T. 1–10) und der Liedweise (C-dorisch, T. 11–33) im Charakter eines Trauermarsches hinzu, die den Stil des ganzen Werkes festlegt.

In den ruhigen Rahmenteilen des zweiten Satzes (T. 1–72 bzw. T. 219–261, jeweils in A) fügt Hindemith das mixolydische Lied *Nun laube, Lindlein, laube* (Böhme Nr. 175) ein:

It appears particularly (bars 35ff) in the simple arpeggio-like theme, interrupted by recitative-like comments from the solo viola. In bars 219ff (horns), on the other hand, Hindemith places the song like a cantus firmus on a transposed reprise of the opening section, a shortened version of the original expository bars. The scherzo-like fugato (F major) of the middle section of this movement is a complete working of the song 'Der Gutzgauch auf dem Zaune sass' (Böhme No. 167; 'Gutzgauch' = 'Kuckuck' = cuckoo):

Zunächst (T. 35ff.) erscheint es im schlichten akkordischen Satz und wird von rezitativischen Einwürfen des Solobratsche unterbrochen. Takt 219ff. (Hörner) hingegen fügt Hindemith das Lied wie einen cantus firmus zur transponierten Reprise des Anfangteils, der um jene das Lied ursprünglich exponierenden Takte gekürzt wird. Das scherzhafte Fugato (F-Dur) des Mittelteils dieses Satzes ist vollständig über das Lied *Der Gutzgauch auf dem Zaune saß* (Böhme Nr. 167; Gutzgauch = Kuckuck) gearbeitet:

At the climax of this section (bars 180ff, trombones; bars 185ff horns; bars 193ff trombones) Hindemith introduced the first part of the song 'Nun laube, Lindlein, laube'.

The third movement (in C major) is presented as a set of variations on the song 'Seid ihr nicht der Schwanendreher'

Auf dem Höhepunkt dieses Abschnitts (T. 180ff. Posaune, T. 185ff. Hörner, T. 193ff. Posaune) fügt Hindemith die erste Zeile des Liedes *Nun laube, Lindlein, laube* hinzu.

Der dritte Satz (in C-Dur) ist als ein Variationssatz über das Lied *Seid ihr nicht der Schwanendreher* (Böhme Nr. 215; nach

(Böhme No. 215; according to Böhme, the 'Schwanendreher' is the keeper of the poultry):

Böhme ist der „Schwanendreher" der Wärter des Geflügels) ausgeführt:

Seid ihr— nicht der Schwa-nen dre - her? Seid ihr nicht der

sel - big' Mann,— seid ihr nicht der sel - big' Mann? So dre - het

mir den Schwan, so hab' ich glau - ben dran, so hab' ich glau-ben dran;

und dreht ihr mir den Schwa - nen nit, seid ihr kein Schwa - nen

dre - her nit; dreht mir den Schwa - nen, dreht mir den Schwa-nen.

In the sketches Hindemith numbered the individual variations with roman numerals: Theme bars 1-26, I 27-46, II 47-77, III 78-102, IV 103-26, V 127-56, VI 157-89, VII 190-209, VIII 210-28, IX 229-48 (the song, in diminution, is treated canonically here), X 249-68. After this bar Hindemith tore a page from the sketch book – on which he had notated an eleventh variation. He then put in a note under bar 268 implying that here bars 103-13 (Variation IV) should be inserted, transposed by a whole tone lower. A twelfth variation followed, with which the version of 1935 also closed, and in which the song is played in full in the solo voice. Hindemith cut this 'Variation XII' in 1936 and composed the definitive, more virtuosic closing section which proceeds from bar 269ff. In this final version bars 269ff serve as eleventh variation and coda.

Hindemith hat in den Skizzen die einzelnen Variationsabschnitte mit römischen Ziffern durchnumeriert: Thema T. 1-26, I 27-46, II 47-77, III 78-102, IV 103-126, V 127-156, VI 157-189, VII 190-209, VIII 210-228, IX 229-248 (das leicht diminuierte Lied wird hier kanonisch geführt), X 249-268. Nach diesem Takt trennte Hindemith im Skizzenbuch eine Seite heraus, auf der eine XI. Variation notiert war. Unter Takt 268 hat er dann eine Notiz eingefügt, der zu entnehmen ist, daß hier die um einen Ganzton tiefer transponierten Takte 103-113 (IV. Variation) eingefügt werden sollen. Es folgt eine XII. Variation, mit der das Werk in der Fassung von 1935 auch geschlossen hat und in der im wesentlichen das Lied in der Solostimme vollständig geführt wird. Diese „XII. Variation" hat Hindemith 1936 gestrichen und jenen definitiven virtuoseren Schlußteil komponiert, der unmittelbar aus den Takten 269ff. hervorgeht. In dieser endgültigen Fassung haben demnach die Takte 269ff. als XI. Variation und Coda zu gelten.

VIII

Hindemith provided a programme note for his concerto (see p. XII), which in its superficial naivety concealed the newness of a modern concerto based on old melodies (in 1935 Alban Berg introduced, among other things, a Kärnten folksong into his Violin Concerto). For only the restitution and the new theoretical understanding of tonality (which, as the epitome of logical tonal relationships, enabled the establishment of musical sense), could make possible the reworking of folk melodies within the modern compositional structure. As early as 1930 Hindemith quoted an old folk melody in the *Konzertmusik* op. 49; the opera *Mathis der Maler* (1932–5) depended heavily on folksong, and the Silesius song 'Du sprichst, das Grosse kann nicht in dem Kleinen sein' (1935) is composed over the cantus firmus 'Es floss ein Ros' vom Himmel herab'. Hindemith writes music that springs from a Romantic soul, but he does not write romantic music.[2]

In *Der Schwanendreher* he reworks, as a 'regular minstrel' who in foreign parts presents the songs of his homeland, the precariousness of his political situation in 1935: the song 'Zwischen Berg und tiefem Tal' is the parting and the pain of leaving; the 'Gutzgauch' is branded as something dangerous in the old folk poetry, something to avoid. And from the song 'Nun laube, Lindlein, laube', Hindemith put into the solo viola exclusively those verses (second movement, bars 202ff, likewise bars 214ff) that contain the words 'I can bear it no longer' similarly 'have a most sorrowful day'. Of course the closing movement continues despite such gloominess: in this music about music making, music making and music push the unfavourable conditions of the time temporarily into the background. 'How nice it is when one can make music',

Hindemith hat seinem Konzept eine programmatische Notiz vorangestellt (vgl. S. XII), die in ihrer vordergründigen Naivität das Neuartige eines modernen Konzertes über alte Weisen verdeckt (1935 hatte auch Alban Berg in sein Violinkonzert u.a. eine Kärntner Volksweise eingefügt). Denn erst die Restituierung und das neue musiktheoretische Verständnis von Tonalität, die als Inbegriff logischer Tonbeziehungen musikalischen Sinn zu stiften vermag, haben das organische Verarbeiten von Volksweisen innerhalb der modernen kompositorischen Faktur ermöglicht. Bereits 1930 zitiert Hindemith im Schlußsatz der *Konzertmusik* op. 49 eine alte Volksweise; die Oper *Mathis der Maler* (1932–35) stützt sich extensiv auf Volkslieder, und das Silesius-Lied *Du sprichst, das Große kann nicht in dem Kleinen sein* (1935) ist über den cantus firmus *Es floß ein Ros' vom Himmel herab* komponiert. Hindemith schreibt eine Musik aus romantischem Geist, aber keine romantische Musik[2].

Im *Schwanendreher* verarbeitet er als „rechter Musikant", der in der Fremde Lieder seiner fernen deutschen Heimat darbringt, unverkennbar seine politisch prekäre Situation um 1935: Das Lied *Zwischen Berg und tiefem Tal* ist eines der Trennung und des Abschiedsschmerzes; der Gutzgauch wird in der alten Volkspoesie als etwas Gefährliches gebrandmarkt, das zu meiden sei. Und aus dem Lied *Nun laube, Lindlein, laube* legt Hindemith in die Solobratsche ausschließlich jene Liedstrophen (II. Satz, T. 202ff. bzw. T. 214ff.), die die Texte *nicht länger ich's ertrag'* bzw. *hab' gar ein' traurig' Tag* führen. Freilich spielt der Schlußsatz über solche Grübeleien hinweg: Musik und Musizieren drängen in dieser Musik über das Musizieren die widrigen Zeitverhältnisse für einen Moment in den Hintergrund. „Wie schön

[2]Rudolf Stephan 'Über Paul Hindemith', in *Hindemith-Jahrbuch, IV, 1974/75*, Mainz 1975, p. 62

[2]Rudolf Stephan *Über Paul Hindemith*, in: *Hindemith-Jahrbuch IV, 1974/75*, Mainz 1975, S. 62

Hindemith wrote to his wife in New York on 2 April 1937, 'and thereby has a more powerful resistance to all the loudness of the old and the new world than all the brooders.'

Giselher Schubert

Translation Penelope Souster

ist's, wenn man Musik machen kann", schreibt Hindemith am 2. April 1937 aus New York seiner Frau, „und damit einen kräftigeren Widerstand gegen alle Lautheit der alten und neuen Welt hat als alle Grübler."

Giselher Schubert

Orchestration / Orchesterbesetzung

Flöte 1, 2
(2. auch kleine Flöte)
Oboe
Klarinette 1, 2
Fagott 1, 2
Horn 1–3
Trompcte
Posaune
Harfe
Pauken
4 Violoncelli
3 Kontrabässe

Sketch of the main theme of the first movement, bars 34 ff
Skizze zum Hauptthema des I. Satzes, Takt 34 ff.

Sketch to second movement, bars 34ff
Skizze zum II. Satz, Takt 34ff.

Programme Note

A minstrel joins a happy gathering and displays what he has brought from distant lands: serious and joyful songs closing with a dance. By his inspiration and skill he extends and decorates the melodies like a regular minstrel, experimenting and improvising.

This medieval picture was the basis for the composition.

Programm-Notiz

Ein Spielmann kommt in frohe Gesellschaft und breitet aus, was er aus der Ferne mitgebracht hat: ernste und heitere Lieder, zum Schluß ein Tanzstück. Nach Einfall und Vermögen erweitert und verziert er als rechter Musikant die Weisen, präludiert und phantasiert.

Dieses mittelalterliche Bild war die Vorlage für die Komposition.

DER SCHWANENDREHER

I. „Zwischen Berg und tiefem Tal"
Langsam (♩ etwa 60)

Paul Hindemith
(1895–1963)

o. 1816   EE 6792

© 1936 Schott Music GmbH & Co. KG, Mainz
© renewed 1964
Ernst Eulenburg & Co GmbH, Mainz

10

11

13

14

16

22

II. „Nun laube, Lindlein, laube!"
Sehr ruhig (♩.etwa 40)

„Der Gutzgauch auf dem Zaune saß"

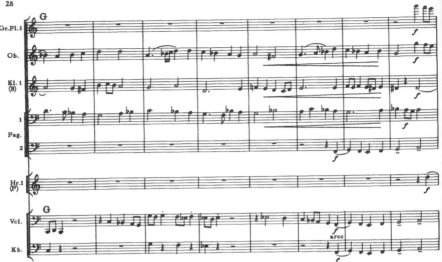

32

III. Variationen „Seid ihr nicht der Schwanendreher"
Mäßig schnell (♩= 100)

38

40

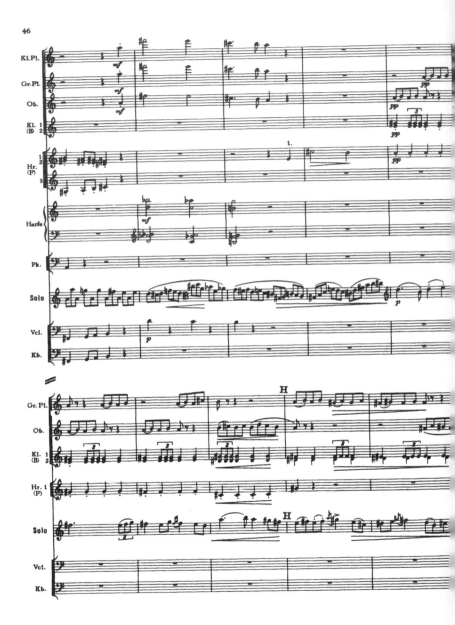

50

Zeitmaß wie früher ($\quad$ = 100)

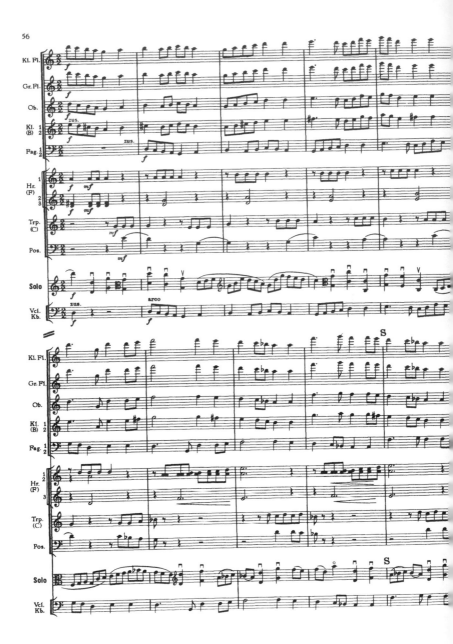

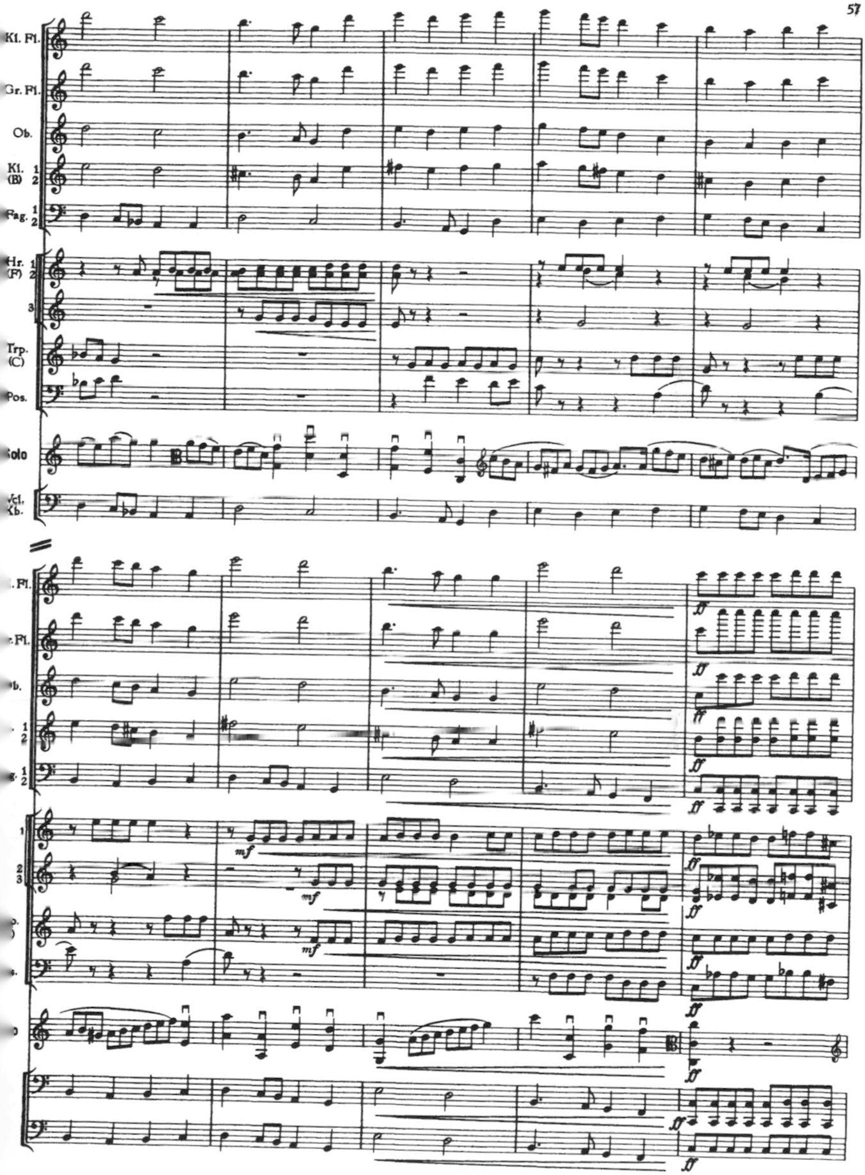
Kl. Fl.
Gr. Fl.
Ob.
Kl. 1 2 (B)
Fag. 1 2
Hr. 1 2 (F)
3
Trp. (C)
Pos.
Solo
Vcl. Kb.
mf
ff